No Nonsense
Maths

9-10 years

Central pull-out pages

Parents' notes   A1
Answers   A2-4

Contents

Recognising and ordering very big numbers

HUNDRED THOUSAND	TEN THOUSAND	THOUSANDS	HUNDREDS	TENS	UNITS
4	3	7	2	6	9

Four hundred and thirty-seven thousand, two hundred and sixty-nine

1. **Match the written number with the correct card. Join the dots.**

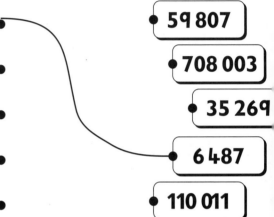

  a Six thousand four hundred and eighty-seven   •   • 59 807

  b Fifty-nine thousand, eight hundred and seven   •   • 708 003

  c Thirty-five thousand, two hundred and sixty-nine   •   • 35 269

  d Seven hundred and eight thousand and three   •   • 6 487

  e One hundred and ten thousand and eleven   •   • 110 011

2. **What number needs to go in the box?**

  a 28 717 = ☐ + 8 000 + 700 + 10 + 7

  b 76 923 = 70 000 + ☐ + 900 + 20 + 3

  c 83 641 = 80 000 + 3 000 + ☐ + 40 + 1

  d 52 876 = 50 000 + 2 000 + 800 + ☐ + 6

  e 39 681 = 30 000 + 9 000 + 600 + 80 + ☐

3. **Write these numbers as words.**

  a 7 623   _____

  b 223 400   _____

  c 78 231   _____

a Put these numbers in order, largest first.

| 2 369 | 223 693 | 26 393 | 93 362 | 6 932 |

b Which two numbers have the digit 2 in the units column?

c Write the number 23 693 in words.

_____

Add the correct 'more than' (>) or 'less than' (<) sign.

a 4 837 ☐ 4 738   **b** 23 687 ☐ 23 678   **c** 286 383 ☐ 268 383

d 86 261 ☐ 86 621   **e** 31 002 ☐ 32 001   **f** 793 976 ☐ 793 796

How many more is ...

a 3 628 than 2 628? _1 000_   **b** 29 345 than 28 345? _____

c 326 516 than 326 416? _____   **d** 268 than 258? _____

| Tough | OK | Got it! | 24 |

Total: 24 / 24

More practice? Go to www

Challenge yourself

a Using each digit only once, make the largest number you can. _____

| 2 | 9 | 6 | 8 | 5 | 3 |

b Write the answer for a in words. _____

_____

c Using each digit only once, make the smallest number you can. _____

d Add 10 000 to this number. _____

3

Negative numbers

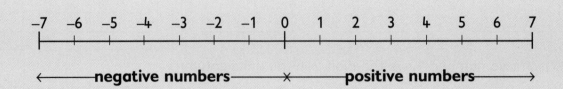

negative numbers ———— × ———— positive numbers

We use negative numbers to measure cold temperatures with a thermometer.

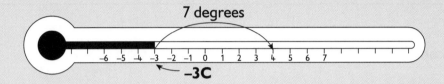

7 degrees

−3C

If the temperature rises from −3°C to 4°C the temperature has risen by 7 degrees.

1. **By how many degrees does the temperature rise?**

a The temperature is −1°C. It rises to 8°C.   _____9_____ degrees

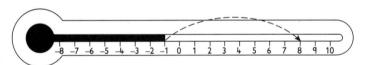

b The temperature is −5°C. It rises to 4°C.   _____ degrees

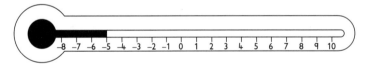

c The temperature is −3°C. It rises to 10°C.   _____ degrees

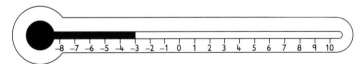

Try these without looking at a thermometer.

d The temperature is −2°C. It rises to 7°C.   _____ degrees

e The temperature is −8°C. It rises to 1°C.   _____ degrees

f The temperature is − 6°C. It rises to 11°C.   _____ degrees

Answer these problems.

a The temperature is 2°C. It falls by 5°C.   What is the temperature now? _____

b The temperature is 6°C. It falls by 10°C.   What is the temperature now? _____

c The temperature is 12°C. It falls by 12°C.   What is the temperature now? _____

Put these numbers in order, lowest first.

a

| −1 | −4 | 0 | 4 | 1 |

_−4_ _____ _____ _____ _____

b

| 6 | −3 | 5 | −2 | 10 |

_____ _____ _____ _____ _____

c

| 2 | −2 | −12 | −22 | 12 |

_____ _____ _____ _____ _____

| Tough | OK | Got it! | **11** |

Total

More practice? Go to www

Challenge yourself

Here are some rows of cards.
Fill in the missing cards so that the five numbers are in order.

a | −6 | −5 | −4 | −3 | −2 |

b | −1 | | 1 | | 3 |

c | −12 | | −10 | | −8 |

d | −3 | | −1 | | 1 |

e | −26 | | −24 | | −22 |

Addition and subtraction

This is how to add large numbers, step by step.

```
  1 6 4        1 6 4        1 6 4
+   2 7      +   2 7      +   2 7
_____    _____    _____
        1          9 1        1 9 1
    ___          ___          ___
      1            1            1
```

There were more than 10 units so 1 ten was carried to the tens column.

1. **Complete these additions.**

a
```
    2 3 6
  +   1 5
  _____

  _____
```

b
```
    1 6 6
  +   2 7
  _____

  _____
```

c
```
    1 8 9
  +   1 7
  _____

  _____
```

In the following questions you will have more than 10 tens, so 1 hundred will have to be carried to the hundreds column.

```
  1 2 7        1 2 7        1 2 7
+ 2 8 4      + 2 8 4      + 2 8 4
_____    _____    _____
        1          1 1        4 1 1
    ___          _____        _____
      1            1 1          1 1
```

2. **Find the answers.**

a
```
    1 3 6
  + 1 7 5
  _____

  _____
```

b
```
    2 1 5
  + 1 9 8
  _____

  _____
```

c
```
    3 6 2
  + 1 7 3
  _____

  _____
```

d
```
    1 7 3
  + 1 6 9
  _____

  _____
```

e
```
    2 3 8
  + 2 9 4
  _____

  _____
```

f
```
    1 7 6
  + 1 5 5
  _____

  _____
```

This is how to subtract large numbers, step by step.

```
    6 1  ○              ⁵ ¹                    ⁵ ¹
                        6̸ 1  ○○○○○○○⊠⊠⊠        6̸ 1
  − 2 4              − 2 4                    − 2 4
  ───────             ───────                 ───────
                          7                      3 7
  ───────             ───────                 ───────
```

If there are not enough units in the top number, change one of the tens to 10 units.

Complete these subtractions.

a   7 2
        − 3 5
        ───────

        ───────

b   6 3
        − 1 8
        ───────

        ───────

c   8 5
        − 3 7
        ───────

        ───────

If there are not enough tens in the top number, change one of the hundreds to 10 tens.

```
                    ⁴ ¹           ⁴ ¹            ² ¹⁴ ¹          ² ¹⁴ ¹
    3 5 4          3̸ 5̸ 4         3̸ 5̸ 4          3̸ 5̸ 4          3̸ 5̸ 4
  − 1 6 7        − 1 6 7       − 1 6 7        − 1 6 7        − 1 6 7
  ─────────      ─────────     ─────────      ─────────      ─────────
                       7             7            8 7          1 8 7
  ─────────      ─────────     ─────────      ─────────      ─────────
```

Find the answers.

a   5 6 2
       − 1 5 9
       ─────────

       ─────────

b   3 5 5
       − 1 6 6
       ─────────

       ─────────

c   6 2 7
       − 2 8 4
       ─────────

       ─────────

Tough	OK	Got it!

15

Total

☐ 15

More practice? Go to

More practice? Go to www

Challenge yourself

Complete these number sentences.

a 642 − _____ = 507

b 228 − _____ = 65

c _____ − 243 = 487

d _____ − 632 = 127

e _____ − 441 = 80

f 462 − _____ = 363

Multiplying and dividing by 10 and 100

When you **multiply** a number by **10**, the digits move **one place to the left**.

$$18 \times 1 = 18$$
$$18 \times 10 = 180$$

When you **divide** a number by **10**, the digits move **one place to the right**.

$$330 \div 1 = 330$$
$$330 \div 10 = 33$$

1. **Complete these number sentences.**

   a $38 \times 10 =$ __380__

   b $72 \times 10 =$ _____

   c $560 \div 10 =$ _____

   d $129 \times 10 =$ _____

   e $380 \div 10 =$ _____

   f $27 \times 10 =$ _____

   g $561 \times 10 =$ _____

   h $190 \div 10 =$ _____

   i $120 \div 10 =$ _____

   j $69 \times 10 =$ _____

   k $230 \div 10 =$ _____

   l $980 \times 10 =$ _____

When you **multiply** a number by **100**, the digits move **two places to the left**.

$$18 \times 1 = 18$$
$$18 \times 10 = 180$$
$$18 \times 100 = 1\,800$$

2. **Multiply these numbers by 100.**

   a $26 \times 100 =$ __2 600__

   b $56 \times 100 =$ _____

   c $41 \times 100 =$ _____

   d $98 \times 100 =$ _____

e 17 × 100 = _____

f 273 × 100 = _____

g 7 951 × 100 = _____

h 1244 × 100 = _____

When you **divide** a number by **100**, the digits move **two places to the right**.

$$300 \div 1 = 300$$
$$300 \div 10 = 30$$
$$\mathbf{300 \div 100 = 3}$$

Divide these numbers by 100.

a 500 ÷ 100 = _____

b 200 ÷ 100 = _____

c 800 ÷ 100 = _____

d 600 ÷ 100 = _____

e 1200 ÷ 100 = _____

f 1700 ÷ 100 = _____

g 2400 ÷ 100 = _____

h 12 900 ÷ 100 = _____

i 53 800 ÷ 100 = _____

j 62 300 ÷ 100 = _____

Tough	OK	Got it!	28

Total

28

More practice? Go to www

Challenge yourself

Answer these questions.

a Jason bought 21 bags of balloons for a big party.
There were 10 balloons in each bag.
How many balloons did he buy altogether? _____

b 2400 paper clips fell on the floor when a piece of
machinery broke in the paper clip factory. A box holds 100 paper clips.
How many boxes of paper clips were lost? _____

c A book has 100 pages. There are 87 words on each page.
How many words are in the book? _____

2, 3, 4, 5, 6, 7, 10 times tables

If you cannot answer one of the times table questions straight away, carry on and come back to it when you have answered the other questions.

1. **How quickly can you answer these multiplication questions?**
Time yourself. Can you do them all in 1 minute?

$2 \times 3 =$ _____ $7 \times 7 =$ _____

$3 \times 5 =$ _____ $5 \times 6 =$ _____

$7 \times 6 =$ _____ $3 \times 3 =$ _____

$4 \times 4 =$ _____ $9 \times 4 =$ _____

$6 \times 7 =$ _____ $10 \times 5 =$ _____

$10 \times 2 =$ _____ $8 \times 6 =$ _____

$8 \times 3 =$ _____ $9 \times 7 =$ _____

$6 \times 6 =$ _____ $5 \times 5 =$ _____

$2 \times 5 =$ _____ $10 \times 4 =$ _____

$10 \times 7 =$ _____ $3 \times 6 =$ _____

$8 \times 2 =$ _____ $1 \times 7 =$ _____

$9 \times 6 =$ _____ $6 \times 4 =$ _____

$7 \times 5 =$ _____ $3 \times 7 =$ _____

$3 \times 4 =$ _____ $9 \times 10 =$ _____

$9 \times 2 =$ _____ $2 \times 4 =$ _____

How long did it take you? _____

Answer these questions.

a What are six sevens? _____

b What is 10 times 8? _____

c What is 5 multiplied by 9? _____

d Multiply six by six. _____

e What is 3 times 9? _____

f What are eight threes? _____

g Multiply five by five. _____

h What is 2 multiplied by 9? _____

i What are four sixes? _____

j What is 4 times 5? _____

k What is 6 multiplied by 8? _____

l Multiply three by seven. _____

| Tough | OK | Got it! | 42 |

Total

42 / 42

More practice? Go to

More practice? Go to www

Challenge yourself

Fill in the boxes.

a $8 \times \boxed{} = 24$

b $\boxed{} \times 5 = 30$

c $6 \times \boxed{} = 24$

d $6 \times \boxed{} = 42$

e $8 \times \boxed{} = 80$

f $10 \times \boxed{} = 100$

g $\boxed{} \times 3 = 21$

h $\boxed{} \times 7 = 49$

i $\boxed{} \times 6 = 36$

j $\boxed{} \times 3 = 18$

k $4 \times \boxed{} = 16$

l $\boxed{} \times 6 = 54$

Time

This timeline uses a 24-hour clock.

1:00 2:00 3:00 4:00 5:00 6:00 7:00 8:00 9:00 10:00 11:00 12:00 13:00 14:00 15:00 16:00 17:00 18:00 19:00 20:00 21:00 22:00 23:00 24:

1. Look at this bus timetable.

Bus stop	Pick-up time		
High Street	12:10	13:10	14:10
Church	12:20	13:20	14:20
Post Office	12:30	13:30	14:30
Sports centre	12:40	13:40	14:40

Answer these questions carefully.

a How many minutes are there between each stop? _____ minutes

b How many minutes does it take the bus to reach the post office after stopping at the

High Street? _____ minutes

c If you missed the bus at 12:30 outside the post office, what time would the next bus

be along? _____

d If you arrived at the church at 2:18, would you be just in time for a bus or too late? _____

e If you arrived at the sports centre at 12:40, how long would you be there if you

caught the 2:40 bus home? _____

f If you had finished shopping in the High Street at 1:13, what time would the

next bus be? _____

Fill in the gaps.

a 1 decade = _____ years

b 1 year = _____ months or _____ weeks or _____ days

c 1 week = _____ days

d 1 day = _____ hours

e 1 hour = _____ minutes

f 1 minute = _____ seconds

Suggest the unit of time (e.g. minutes, days, years, etc.) that would be used for the following:

a to boil a kettle _____

b to walk across a road _____

c to grow from a baby into a 10-year-old _____

d to have a birthday party _____

e to fly to France _____

			Total
Tough	OK	Got it! **17**	

More practice? Go to

Challenge yourself

Solve these problems.

a Titus got up at 08:10.
He left for school 40 minutes later.
His journey took 20 minutes.
School starts at 09:00.

Was Titus late? _____

If so, by how many minutes? _____

b The Chichester Colts football team kicked off at 14:30. They played 45 minutes each way and had a 15 minute break at half-time. At what time did the game finish? _____

(P.S. The Chichester Colts won 2–1!)

Length

1 kilometre (km) = 1000 metres
1 metre (m)   = 100 centimetres
1 centimetre (cm) = 10 millimetres (mm)

⌐___⌐ 1 cm   ⊔⊔⊔⊔⊔ 10 mm

1. **Underline the nearest correct measurement in each sentence. Do you think ...**

a	your table is	1 m ,	2 m	or	30 m long?
b	this page is	5 cm,	15 cm	or	21 cm wide?
c	the ceiling is	3 m,	6 m	or	9 m high?
d	your pencil or pen is	1 mm,	7 mm	or	15 mm wide?
e	a house is	2 m,	4 m	or	15 m high?

2. **Suggest things you would measure in ...**

   a kilometres _____   _____

   b metres ____playground____   _____

   c centimetres _____   _____

   d millimetres _____   _____

3. **Which unit of measure would you use to measure ...**

   a your height? _____

   b the length of a ship? _____

   c the distance from Chichester to London? _____

   d the width of a frisbee? _____

   e the width of a paper clip? _____

What is the distance between the two arrows?

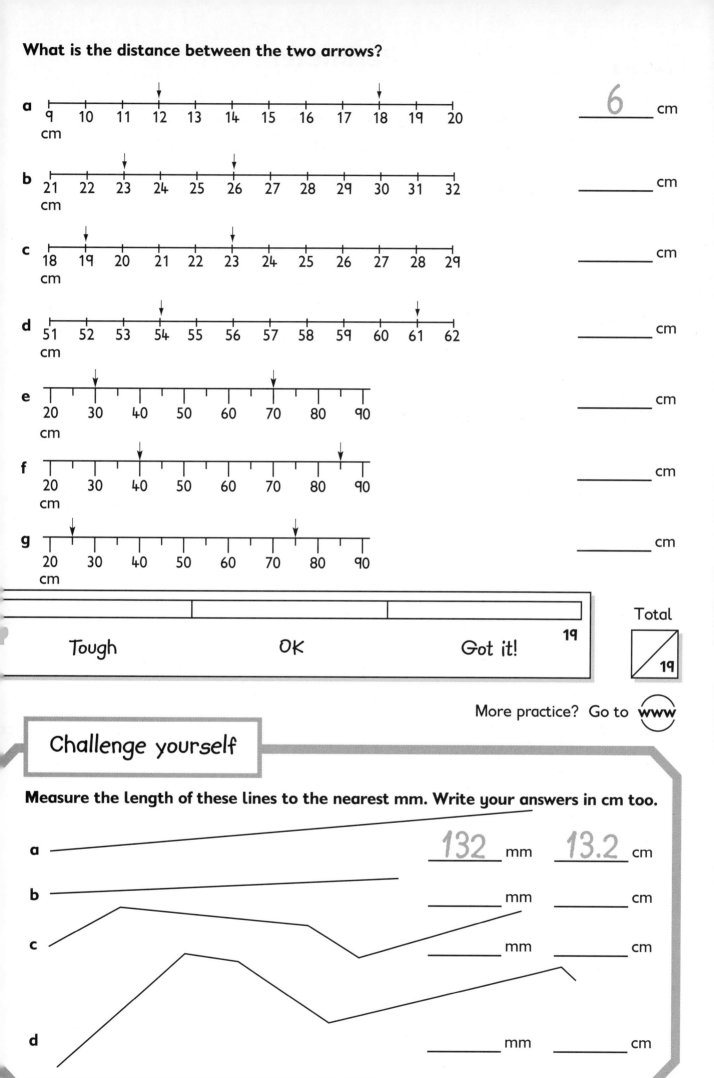

a _____ <u>6</u> cm

b _____ cm

c _____ cm

d _____ cm

e _____ cm

f _____ cm

g _____ cm

Tough	OK	Got it! **19**

Total

19 / 19

More practice? Go to www

Challenge yourself

Measure the length of these lines to the nearest mm. Write your answers in cm too.

a _____ <u>132</u> mm <u>13.2</u> cm

b _____ mm _____ cm

c _____ mm _____ cm

d _____ mm _____ cm

Perimeter

The **perimeter** is the distance around the outside edge of a shape.

3 cm

2 cm

3 cm + 2 cm + 3 cm + 2 cm = 10 cm

The perimeter is 10 cm.
Opposite sides of a rectangle are the same length.

1. **Find the perimeter of each shape.**

7 cm

a 3 cm

7 cm + 3 cm + 7 cm + 3 cm = ___20___ cm

5 cm

b 4 cm

= _____ cm

12 cm

c 1 cm

= _____ cm

4 cm

d 4 cm   3 cm

1 cm

5 cm

= _____ cm

3 cm

5 cm

e   8 cm

5 cm

3 cm

= _____ cm

Measure the perimeters of these letters.

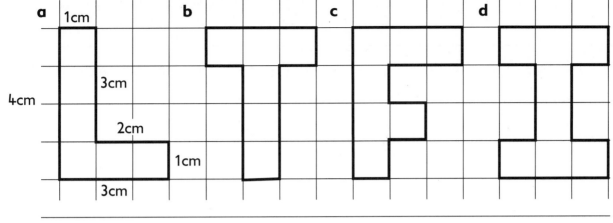

a __14__ cm   b _____ cm   c _____ cm   d _____ cm

What is the perimeter of ...

Parklands playground

a the playground? _____ m

b the climbing frame? _____ m

c the netball court? _____ m

scale: 1 cm = 3 m

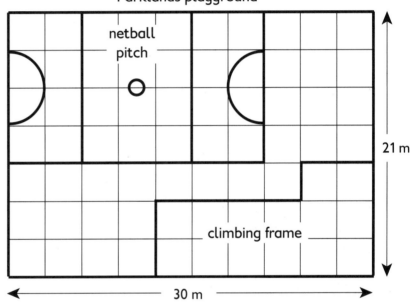

netball pitch

climbing frame

21 m

30 m

Challenge yourself

Solve these problems.

a The perimeter of a rectangle is 30 cm. The shortest side is 5 cm.
What is the length of the longer sides? _____ cm

b The perimeter of a rectangle is 42 cm. The shortest side is 6 cm.
What is the length of the longer sides? _____ cm

Which operation? +, –, ×, ÷

When considering a problem, it is not always easy to know which operation to use. Always read the problem carefully and try to visualise what it is asking.

It is also useful to remember the different terms that can be used in connection with each operation.

+	add	sum	total	altogether
–	take away	subtract	difference between	how many are left
×	times	multiply	product	multiplied by
÷	share	group	divide	divided into

1. Solve these problems.

a There are 6 eggs in each box.

How many eggs in 9 boxes? _____

How many boxes would 42 eggs fill? _____

b I think of a number and then subtract 16.
The answer is 28.

What was my number? _____

c Tuhil has 46 marbles.
Tina has half as many.

How many marbles does Tina have? _____

d In the school library there are 136 books on the top shelf.
There are 112 on the bottom shelf.
Caroline takes 32 books for a class project.

How many books are left? _____

e Mark started to read a book on Monday.
On Tuesday he read 10 more pages than on Monday.
He reached page 50.

How many pages did he read on Monday? _____

f Think of a number, subtract 12 and divide by 3.
The answer is 10.

What was the number? _____

Which operation sign goes in each box?

a 235 ☐ 69 = 304

b 520 ☐ 10 = 52

c 986 ☐ 235 = 751

d 56 ☐ 8 = 448

e 566 ☐ 245 = 321

f 38 ☐ 38 = 1444

g 4 005 ☐ 45 = 89

h 254 ☐ 364 = 618

i 456 ☐ 3 = 1 368

j 786 ☐ 658 = 128

k 233 ☐ 13 = 3 029

l 132 ☐ 7 = 924

| Tough | OK | Got it! | 18 |

Total

☐ 18

More practice? Go to www

Challenge yourself

Look at questions 1b and 1f in this lesson.
Write two similar problems and test them on your friends or family.
(You need to work backwards!)

a I think of a number and then _____

The answer is _____

What was my number? _____

b I think of a number and then _____

The answer is _____

What was my number? _____

How am I doing?

1. Write the missing numbers.

a $36\,542 = $ _____ $ + 6\,000 + 500 + 40 + 2$

b $78\,336 = 70\,000 + $ _____ $ + 300 + 30 + 6$

c $58\,061 = 50\,000 + 8\,000 + $ _____ $ + 60 + 1$

d $21\,654 = 20\,000 + 1\,000 + 600 + $ _____ $ + 4$

e $92\,835 = 90\,000 + 2\,000 + 800 + 30 + $ _____

2. Put these numbers in order, lowest first.

a | 3 | | −3 | | 2 | | −2 | | 1 |

___ ___ ___ ___ ___

b | 7 | | −17 | | −7 | | 0 | | 17 |

___ ___ ___ ___ ___

3. Complete these calculations.

a $\begin{array}{r} 2\,3\,5 \\ +\ 1\,1\,7 \\ \hline \end{array}$

b $\begin{array}{r} 6\,2\,5 \\ +\ 2\,9\,6 \\ \hline \end{array}$

c $\begin{array}{r} 3\,1\,6 \\ +\ 1\,7\,5 \\ \hline \end{array}$

d $\begin{array}{r} 5\,2\,8 \\ +\ 2\,6\,9 \\ \hline \end{array}$

e $\begin{array}{r} 7\,3 \\ -\ 2\,6 \\ \hline \end{array}$

f $\begin{array}{r} 3\,4\,4 \\ -\ 1\,7\,7 \\ \hline \end{array}$

g $\begin{array}{r} 5\,2 \\ -\ 2\,9 \\ \hline \end{array}$

h $\begin{array}{r} 4\,2\,8 \\ -\ 1\,6\,5 \\ \hline \end{array}$

4. Find the answers.

a $41 \times 10 = $ _____

b $460 \div 10 = $ _____

c $28 \times 100 = $ _____

d $3\,700 \div 100 = $ _____

e $62 \times 10 = $ _____

f $170 \div 10 = $ _____

g $57 \times 100 = $ _____

h $2\,800 \div 100 = $ _____

i $39 \times 10 = $ _____

j $230 \div 10 = $ _____

Fill in the gaps.

a $6 \times$ _____ $= 18$

b $2 \times$ _____ $= 6$

c $9 \times$ _____ $= 54$

d $7 \times$ _____ $= 42$

e _____ $\times 5 = 50$

f $3 \times$ _____ $= 15$

g $8 \times$ _____ $= 32$

h _____ $\times 4 = 28$

i $3 \times$ _____ $= 27$

Join the dots to match each activity with the correct unit of time.

a Cycle 155 times around the playground ●

b Eat a bag of crisps ●

c Climb out of bed ●

● seconds

● hours

● minutes

What is the distance between the two arrows?

a 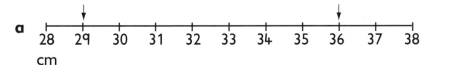 _____ cm

b 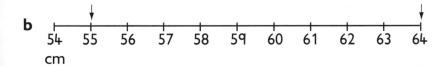 _____ cm

Work out the perimeter of each shape.

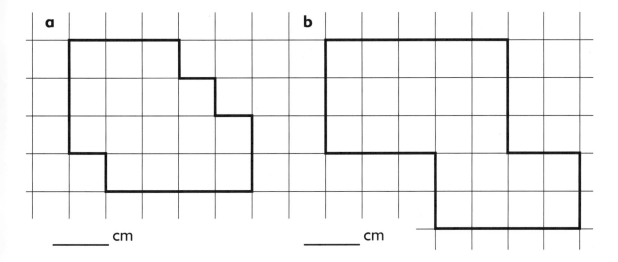

a _____ cm

b _____ cm

Which sign? $+$, $-$, x, $\div$

a $126 \;\boxed{}\; 361 = 487$

b $272 \;\boxed{}\; 17 = 16$

c $689 \;\boxed{}\; 98 = 591$

d $34 \;\boxed{}\; 126 = 4\,284$

Total

$\boxed{45}$

More practice? Go to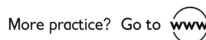

Number bonds

$$72 + ? = 100$$

Adding numbers to 100 is easier than it looks.
First, in your head, the units need to add up to 10.

$$\begin{array}{r} 72 \\ +\ 8 \\ \hline 0 \\ \hline {\scriptstyle 1} \end{array}$$

Next, the tens need to add up to 10.

$$\begin{array}{r} 72 \\ +\ 28 \\ \hline 100 \\ \hline {\scriptstyle 1} \end{array}$$

$$72 + 28 = 100$$

1. **Complete these number sentences.**

a $36 +$ _____ $= 100$

b _____ $+ 51 = 100$

c $79 +$ _____ $= 100$

d _____ $+ 97 = 100$

e $63 +$ _____ $= 100$

f _____ $+ 26 = 100$

g $25 +$ _____ $= 100$

h _____ $+ 86 = 100$

i $81 +$ _____ $= 100$

j _____ $+ 49 = 100$

k _____ $+ 56 = 100$

l $71 +$ _____ $= 100$

m _____ $+ 37 = 100$

n $32 +$ _____ $= 100$

o _____ $+ 11 = 100$

p $68 +$ _____ $= 100$

q _____ $+ 76 = 100$

r $57 +$ _____ $= 100$

How quickly can you do these?

a 10 + 10 = _____

b 12 + 12 = _____

c 15 + 15 = _____

d 7 + 7 = _____

e 21 + 21 = _____

f 17 + 17 = _____

g 11 + 11 = _____

h 14 + 14 = _____

i 23 + 23 = _____

j 31 + 31 = _____

k 26 + 26 = _____

l 19 + 19 = _____

m 25 + 25 = _____

n 38 + 38 = _____

o 47 + 47 = _____

p 29 + 29 = _____

Fill in the gaps. In each case, the two numbers need to be the same.

a 26 = _____ + _____

b 40 = _____ + _____

c 54 = _____ + _____

d 100 = _____ + _____

e 78 = _____ + _____

f 64 = _____ + _____

			Total
Tough	OK	Got it! 40	40/40

More practice? Go to www

Challenge yourself

The first answer will help you with the second answer!

a 7 + 7 = _____   70 + 70 = _____

b 23 + 23 = _____   230 + 230 = _____

c 18 + 18 = _____   180 + 180 = _____

d 31 + 31 = _____   310 + 310 = _____

e 46 + 46 = _____   460 + 460 = _____

f 27 + 27 = _____   270 + 270 = _____

Round a number to the nearest 10, 100 or 1 000

Do you remember?

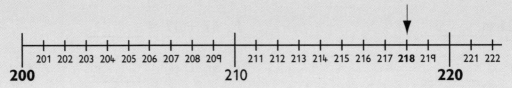

218 rounded to the nearest **ten** is **220**.
218 rounded to the nearest **hundred** is **200**.

1. **Fill in the gaps in the following sentences.**

   a 237 rounded to the nearest ten is _____.

   237 rounded to the nearest hundred is _____.

   b 382 rounded to the nearest ten is _____.

   382 rounded to the nearest hundred is _____.

   c 769 rounded to the nearest ten is _____.

   769 rounded to the nearest hundred is _____.

2. **Put a circle around the best approximation for the following number sentences.**

   a 609 + 92 = ?

   | 600 + 100 | 700 + 90 | (610 + 90) | 600 + 90 |

   b 413 + 87 = ?

   | 410 + 80 | 400 + 80 | 410 + 90 | 410 + 100 |

   c 389 + 69 = ?

   | 380 + 70 | 400 + 70 | 390 + 70 | 390 + 60 |

   d 762 + 155 = ?

   | 770 + 150 | 770 + 160 | 760 + 160 | 760 + 150 |

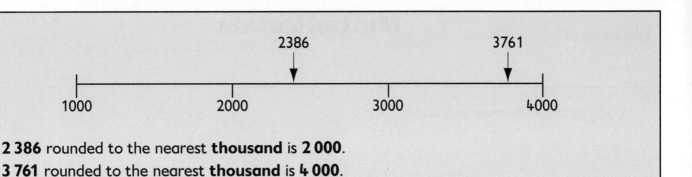

2 386 rounded to the nearest **thousand** is **2 000**.
3 761 rounded to the nearest **thousand** is **4 000**.

Round these numbers to the nearest thousand.

a 1863 rounded to the nearest thousand is _____.

b 5 216 rounded to the nearest thousand is _____.

c 7 777 rounded to the nearest thousand is _____.

d 8 500 rounded to the nearest thousand is _____.

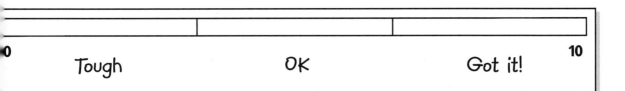

| Tough | OK | Got it! |

0   10

Total

More practice? Go to www

Challenge yourself

Round these distances from London to the ...

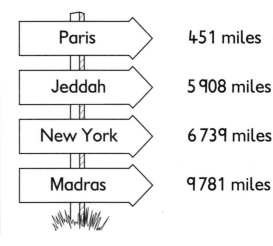

	nearest 10 miles	nearest 100 miles	nearest 1000 miles
Paris	450		
Jeddah			6 000
New York		6 700	
Madras			

Paris   451 miles

Jeddah   5 908 miles

New York   6 739 miles

Madras   9 781 miles

a Which place would you be visiting if you travelled approximately 6 000 miles?

_____

b Which place would you be visiting if you travelled approximately 10 000 miles?

_____

25

Multiplication

Look at these number sentences.

$3 \times 4 = 12$ $7 \times 6 = 42$

$3 \times 40 = 120$ $70 \times 6 = 420$

If a number in a number sentence is in the ten times table, the answer is also in the ten times table.

QUICK TIP!
Knowing this can help with long multiplication!

1. **Complete these number sentences.**

   a $5 \times 5 =$ _____

   $50 \times 5 =$ _____

   b $8 \times 4 =$ _____

   $8 \times 40 =$ _____

   c $9 \times 7 =$ _____

   $90 \times 7 =$ _____

   d $6 \times 3 =$ _____

   $6 \times 30 =$ _____

   e $4 \times 2 =$ _____

   $40 \times 2 =$ _____

   f $7 \times 6 =$ _____

   $7 \times 60 =$ _____

2. **Now try these.**

   a $40 \times 3 =$ _____

   b $8 \times 70 =$ _____

   c $50 \times 4 =$ _____

   d $3 \times 90 =$ _____

   e $60 \times 2 =$ _____

   f $7 \times 50 =$ _____

   g $40 \times 9 =$ _____

   h $3 \times 80 =$ _____

Do you remember?

$$\begin{array}{r} 26 \\ \times\ \ 6 \\ \hline 120 \\ 36 \\ \hline 156 \\ \hline \end{array}$$

120 (20×6)

36 (6×6)

156 (26×6)

Complete these multiplications.

a   34
   × 3

   90 (30 × 3)
   12   (4 × 3)
        (34 × 3)

b   45
   × 4

        (40 × 4)
        (5 × 4)
        (45 × 4)

c   63
   × 5

        (60 × 5)
        (3 × 5)
        (63 × 5)

d   23
   × 2

e   45
   × 5

f   27
   × 6

g   41
   × 7

h   63
   × 6

i   52
   × 7

Tough	OK	Got it!

Total

22

22

More practice? Go to www

More practice? Go to www

Challenge yourself

Solve these problems.

a   Nanny Dawn had six grandchildren. She decided to give each of them 45p.

    How much money did Nanny Dawn give her grandchildren altogether? _____

b   Tina, Mick and Matthew each bought a book. Two of the books have 84 pages.
    One book has 80 pages.

    How many pages do the books have altogether? _____

Division

Remember, we can write a division calculation in different ways.

$$95 \div 5 = 19$$

$$5\overline{\smash{)}95} \quad \text{(19)}$$

We divide larger numbers like this:

First we ask how many 5s in 9
= 1 r 4
(We carry the 4 to the next column)

$$5\overline{\smash{)}9\,^4 5} \quad \text{(1)}$$

Now we ask how many 5s in 45

= 9

$$5\overline{\smash{)}9\,^4 5} \quad \text{(1 9)}$$

1. Divide the following.

a $4\overline{\smash{)}72}$

b $6\overline{\smash{)}90}$

c $3\overline{\smash{)}57}$

d $7\overline{\smash{)}91}$

e $4\overline{\smash{)}64}$

f $5\overline{\smash{)}85}$

2. Find the answers to these number sentences.
Use the space provided to work out your answers.

a $48 \div 2 = \underline{\hspace{1cm}}$

b $75 \div 5 = \underline{\hspace{1cm}}$

c $90 \div 6 = \underline{\hspace{1cm}}$

d $68 \div 4 = \underline{\hspace{1cm}}$

e $120 \div 5 = \underline{\hspace{1cm}}$

f $182 \div 7 = \underline{\hspace{1cm}}$

Divide the following.

Watch out, some of these division number sentences will have remainders!

a 77 ÷ 3 = _____ r ____

b 127 ÷ 6 = _____ r ____

c 130 ÷ 4 = _____ r ____

d 73 ÷ 2 = _____ r ____

e 149 ÷ 5 = _____ r ____

f 219 ÷ 7 = _____ r ____

Tough	OK	Got it! **18**	

0

Total

18

More practice? Go to

More practice? Go to www

Challenge yourself

Solve these problems.

a Moira Jackman bought a packet of sweets to share equally between her four children.

There are 66 sweets in the packet. How many sweets will each of her children get?

_____

Are there any sweets left over? _____

b Farmer Tom has 144 sheep. He divides them equally between six fields.

How many sheep does he have in each field? _____

The following week he buys another 12 sheep. If he also divides these sheep equally

between the fields, how many sheep will he now have in each field? _____

Calculations

There is always a way of checking a $+$, $-$, $\times$ or $\div$ calculation.

Look at these number sentences.

$$38 + 71 = 109 \longrightarrow 109 - 71 = 38$$
$$268 - 126 = 142 \longrightarrow 126 + 142 = 268$$

1. **Complete the second number sentence, by using the information in the first.**

a $42 + 56 = 98$ $98 - \underline{56} = 42$

b $71 + 28 = 99$ $99 - 71 = \underline{}$

c $136 + 78 = 214$ $214 - 136 = \underline{}$

d $93 - 21 = 72$ $72 + 21 = \underline{}$

e $114 - 24 = 90$ $24 + \underline{} = 114$

f $236 + 84 = 320$ $320 - \underline{} = 236$

g $79 + 156 = 235$ $235 - \underline{} = 79$

h $387 - 189 = 198$ $198 + 189 = \underline{}$

Look at these number sentences.

$$27 \times 3 = 81 \longrightarrow 81 \div 3 = 27$$
$$216 \div 36 = 6 \longrightarrow 36 \times 6 = 216$$

2. **Complete the second number sentence, by using the information in the first.**

a $56 \times 3 = 168$ $168 \div 3 = \underline{56}$

b $186 \div 6 = 31$ $31 \times 6 = \underline{}$

c $702 \div 78 = 9$ $\underline{} \times 9 = 702$

d $29 \times 7 = 203$ $203 \div 29 = \underline{\hspace{2cm}}$

e $96 \times 12 = 1\,152$ $1152 \div 12 = \underline{\hspace{2cm}}$

f $448 \div 56 = 8$ $56 \times \underline{\hspace{2cm}} = 448$

g $432 \div 12 = 36$ $36 \times 12 = \underline{\hspace{2cm}}$

h $78 \times 15 = 1\,170$ $1170 \div 15 = \underline{\hspace{2cm}}$

Is the second number sentence in each pair right? Put a ✓ for right or ✗ for wrong.

a $2\,187 + 1\,968 = 4\,155$ $4\,155 - 1\,968 = 2\,187$ ☐

b $28 \times 32 = 896$ $896 \div 29 = 32$ ☐

c $568 - 89 = 479$ $89 + 478 = 568$ ☐

d $5\,320 \div 266 = 20$ $266 \times 20 = 5\,320$ ☐

e $1876 + 549 = 2\,425$ $2\,425 - 549 = 1\,877$ ☐

f $459 \times 21 = 9\,639$ $9\,639 \div 21 = 458$ ☐

Tough	OK	Got it!	20

Total

0   20

More practice? Go to **www**

Challenge yourself

Complete the calculation pairs.

a $6\,888 \div 123 = \underline{\hspace{2cm}}$ $123 \times 56 = \underline{\hspace{2cm}}$

b $\underline{\hspace{2cm}} + 589 = 1\,178$ $1178 - \underline{\hspace{2cm}} = 589$

c $78 \times \underline{\hspace{2cm}} = 38\,142$ $\underline{\hspace{2cm}} \div 489 = 78$

d $4\,444 - 363 = \underline{\hspace{2cm}}$ $\underline{\hspace{2cm}} + 4\,081 = 4\,444$

8 times table

4 lots of 8 is 32

$$+ \quad + \quad + \quad = 32$$

8   8   8   8

4 × 8 = 32

1. $1 \times 8 =$ _____ $6 \times 8 =$ _____

   $2 \times 8 =$ _____ $7 \times 8 =$ _____

   $3 \times 8 =$ _____ $8 \times 8 =$ _____

   $4 \times 8 =$ _____ $9 \times 8 =$ _____

   $5 \times 8 =$ _____ $10 \times 8 =$ _____

2. **Finish the 8 times table number sequences.**

   a
8		24			48		

   b
24			56		72	

   c
16						72

No Nonsense
Maths

9–10 years

Parents' notes

What your child will learn from this book

Bond No Nonsense will help your child to understand and become more confident in their maths work. This book features all the main maths objectives covered by your child's class teacher during the school year. It provides clear, straightforward teaching and learning of the essentials in a rigorous, step-by-step way.

How you can help

Following a few simple guidelines will ensure that your child gets the best from this book:

- Explain that the book will help your child become confident in their maths work.
- If your child has difficulty reading the text on the page or understanding a question, do provide help.
- Provide scrap paper to give your child extra space for rough working.
- Encourage your child to complete all the exercises in a lesson. You can mark the work using this answer section (which you will also find on the website). Your child can record their own impressions of the work using the 'How did I do?' feature.

| 0 | Tough | OK | Got it! | 19 |

- The 'How am I doing?' sections provide a further review of progress.

Using the website – www.bondlearning.co.uk

- The website provides extra practice of every skill in the book. So if your child does not feel confident about a lesson, they can go to the website and have another go.
- For every page of this book you will find further practice questions and their answers available to download.
- To access the extra practice pages:
  1. Go to www.bondlearning.co.uk
  2. Click on 'Maths'.
  3. Click on '9–10 years'.
  4. Click on the lesson you want.

Bond No Nonsense 9–10 years Answers

(1) Recognising and ordering very big numbers pp2–3

1 b 59 807　c 35 269　d 708 003　e 110 011
2 a 20 000　b 6 000　c 600　d 70　e 1
3 a seven thousand, six hundred and twenty-three
　b two hundred and twenty-three thousand, four hundred
　c seventy-eight thousand, two hundred and thirty-one
4 a 223 693　93 362　26 393　6 932　2 369　b 6 932　93 362
　c twenty-three thousand, six hundred and ninety-three
5 a >　b >　c >　d <　e <　f >
6 b 1000　c 100　d 10

Challenge yourself
a 986 532
b nine hundred and eighty-six thousand, five hundred and thirty-two
c 235 689　d 245 689

(2) Negative numbers pp4–5

1 b 9　c 13　d 9　e 9　f 17
2 a −3°C　b −4°C　c 0°C
3 a −4 −1 0 1 4　b −3 −2 5 6 10　c −22 −12 −2 2 12

Challenge yourself
b 0 2　c −11 −9　d −2 0　e −25 −23

(3) Addition and subtraction pp6–7

1 a 251　b 193　c 206
2 a 311　b 413　c 535　d 342　e 532　f 331
3 a 37　b 45　c 48
4 a 403　b 189　c 343

Challenge yourself
a 135　b 163　c 730　d 759　e 521　f 99

(4) Multiplying and dividing by 10 and 100 pp8–9

1 b 720　c 56　d 1290　e 38　f 270　g 5 610
　h 19　i 12　j 690　k 23　l 9 800
2 b 5 600　c 4 100　d 9 800　e 1 700　f 27 300
　g 795 100　h 124 400
3 a 5　b 2　c 8　d 6　e 12　f 17
　g 24　h 129　i 538　j 623

Challenge yourself
a 210　b 24　c 8 700

(5) 2, 3, 4, 5, 6, 7, 10 times tables pp10–11

1 6 49 15 30 42 9 16 36 42 50 20 48 24 63 36 25 10 40
　70 18 16 7 54 24 35 21 12 90 18 8
2 a 42　b 80　c 45　d 36　e 27　f 24　g 25　h 18
　i 24　j 20　k 48　l 21

Challenge yourself
a 3　b 6　c 4　d 7　e 10　f 10　g 7　h 7　i 6
j 6　k 4　l 9

(6) Time pp12–13

1 a 10　b 20　c 13:30　d in time
　e 2 hours　f 14:10
2 a 10 years　b 12 months or 52 weeks or 365 days
　c 7 days　d 24 hours　e 60 minutes　f 60 seconds
3 a minutes　b seconds　c years　d hours
　e hours

Challenge yourself
a Yes, 10 minutes　b 16:15

(7) Length pp14–15

1 b 21 cm　c 3 m　d 7 mm　e 15 m
2 Answers will vary
3 a cm or m　b m　c km　d cm　e mm
4 b 3 cm　c 4 cm　d 7 cm　e 40 cm　f 45 cm
　g 50 cm

Challenge yourself
b 95 mm 9.5 cm　c 135 mm 13.5 cm　d 160 mm 16 cm

(8) Perimeter pp16–17

1 b 18 cm　c 26 cm　d 17 cm　e 24 cm
2 b 14 cm　c 16 cm　d 18 cm
3 a 102 m　b 54 m　c 66 m

Challenge yourself
a 10 cm　b 15 cm

(9) Which operation? +, −, ×, ÷ pp18–19

1 a 54, 7　b 44　c 23　d 216　e 20　f 42
2 a +　b ÷　c −　d ×　e −　f ×
　g ÷　h +　i ×　j −　k ×　l ×

Challenge yourself
Answers will vary

How am I doing? pp20–21

1 a 30 000　b 8 000　c 0　d 50　e 5
2 a −3 −2 1 2 3　b −17 −7 0 7 17
3 a 352　b 921　c 491　d 797　e 47　f 167
　g 23　h 263
4 a 410　b 46　c 2 800　d 37　e 620　f 17
　g 5 700　h 28　i 390　j 23
5 a 3　b 3　c 6　d 6　e 10　f 5
　g 4　h 7　i 9
6 a hours　b minutes　c seconds
7 a 7 cm　b 9 cm
8 a 18 cm　b 24 cm
9 a +　b ÷　c −　d x

(10) Number bonds pp22–23

1 a 64　b 49　c 21　d 3　e 37　f 74　g 75
　h 14　i 19　j 51　k 44　l 29　m 63　n 68
　o 89　p 32　q 24　r 43
2 a 20　b 24　c 30　d 14　e 42　f 34　g 22
　h 28　i 46　j 62　k 52　l 38　m 50　n 76
　o 94　p 58
3 a 13 + 13　b 20 + 20　c 27 + 27　d 50 + 50
　e 39 + 39　f 32 + 32

Challenge yourself
a 14, 140　b 46, 460　c 36, 360　d 62, 620　e 92, 920
f 54, 540

(11) Round a number to the nearest 10, 100 or 1 000 pp24–25

1 a 240, 200　b 380, 400　c 770, 800
2 b 410 + 90　c 390 + 70　d 760 + 160
3 a 2 000　b 5 000　c 8 000　d 9 000

Challenge yourself

	nearest 10 miles	nearest 100 miles	nearest 1000 miles
Paris	450	500	0
Jeddah	5 910	5 900	6 000
New York	6 740	6 700	7 000
Madras	9 780	9 800	10 000

a Jeddah　b Madras

(12) Multiplication pp26–27

1 a 25, 250　b 32, 320　c 63, 630　d 18, 180　e 8, 80
　f 42, 420
2 a 120　b 560　c 200　d 270　e 120
　f 350　g 360　h 240
3 a 102　b 160, 20, 180　c 300, 15, 315

d 46   e 225   f 162   g 287   h 378   i 364

Challenge yourself
£2.70   b 248

3 Division pp28–29
a 18   b 15   c 19   d 13   e 16   f 17
a 24   b 15   c 15   d 17   e 24   f 26
a 25 r2   b 21 r1   c 32 r2   d 36 r1   e 29 r4   f 31 r2

Challenge yourself
16, 2   b 24, 26

4 Calculations pp30–31
b 28   c 78   d 93   e 90   f 84   g 156   h 387
b 186   c 78   d 7   e 96   f 8   g 432   h 78
a ✓   b ✗   c ✗   d ✓   e ✗   f ✗

Challenge yourself
56, 6888   b 589, 589   c 489, 38 142   d 4081, 363

5 8 times table pp32–33
8, 16, 24, 32, 40, 48, 56, 64, 72, 80

a | 8 | 16 | 24 | 32 | 40 | 48 | 56 | 64 |

b | 24 | 32 | 40 | 48 | 56 | 64 | 72 | 80 |

c | 16 | 24 | 32 | 40 | 48 | 56 | 64 | 72 |

a 48   b 24   c 64   d 56   e 0   f 80
a 32   b 72   c 56   d 64   e 48   f 48   g 0   h 40

Challenge yourself
10   b 8   c 2   d 0   e 8   f 4   g 8   h 8   i 1
6   k 3   l 9

6 Fractions pp34–35
b 10   c 6
a 5   b 2   c 8   d 6   e 5   f 7   g 21   h 9
i 5   j 9

b $\frac{1}{10}$ $\frac{1}{5}$ $\frac{1}{3}$ c $\frac{1}{6}$ $\frac{1}{4}$ $\frac{1}{3}$ d $\frac{2}{9}$ $\frac{1}{2}$ $\frac{3}{4}$ e $\frac{1}{5}$ $\frac{3}{10}$ $\frac{2}{3}$

f $\frac{1}{6}$ $\frac{1}{3}$ $\frac{2}{4}$ g $\frac{1}{6}$ $\frac{2}{10}$ $\frac{5}{9}$ h $\frac{1}{5}$ $\frac{1}{4}$ $\frac{3}{10}$

b $\frac{2}{7}$ c $\frac{4}{8}$ or $\frac{1}{2}$ d $\frac{3}{9}$ or $\frac{1}{3}$ e $\frac{2}{8}$ or $\frac{1}{4}$

Challenge yourself
$\frac{1}{5}$ b $\frac{2}{7}$ c $\frac{3}{4}$ d $\frac{8}{10}$ or $\frac{4}{5}$

7 Mass pp36–37
a 3 kg   b 5 g   c 1 g   d 3 kg   e 80 g
Answers will vary
a grams   b grams   c kilograms   d grams
e grams   f kilograms
b 80 kg   c 20 kg   d 50 kg   e 70 kg   f 30 kg

Challenge yourself
0 g flour   100 g fat   150 g sugar   4 tbsp treacle
tsp ground ginger

8 Area pp38–39
b 14 cm²   c 40 cm²   d 18 cm²
e 7 cm × 5 cm = 35 cm²   f 10 cm × 2 cm = 20 cm²
a 30 cm²   b 36 cm²   c 56 cm²   d 90 cm²

Challenge yourself
Answers will vary (18 cm² on each side)

9 Shape pp40–41
a isosceles   b scalene   c right-angled
Answers will vary
square or rectangle
Answers will vary   Examples: a cereal box   b dice
c baked bean tin   d ball
a cube   b cuboid   c cylinder   d triangular prism

Challenge yourself

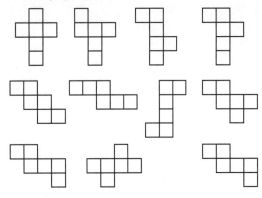

How am I doing? pp42–43
1 a 43   b 72   c 83   d 1
2 a 370   b 700   c 4000
3 a
$$\begin{array}{r} 23 \\ \times\ 4 \\ \hline 80\ (20\times4) \\ 12\ (3\times4) \\ \hline 92\ (23\times4) \end{array}$$
b
$$\begin{array}{r} 56 \\ \times\ 5 \\ \hline 250\ (50\times5) \\ 30\ (6\times5) \\ \hline 280\ (56\times5) \end{array}$$
c
$$\begin{array}{r} 72 \\ \times\ 6 \\ \hline 420\ (70\times6) \\ 12\ (2\times6) \\ \hline 432\ (72\times6) \end{array}$$

4 a 13   b 16   c 24   d 15 r1   e 12 r6   f 25 r2
5 a 117   b 27   c 456   d 1064
6 a 24   b 72   c 56   d 32   e 40   f 80
7 a 3   b 5   c 12   d 6   e 4   f 2
8 a 20 kg   b 60 kg   c 30 kg
9 a 3 cm × 6 cm = 18 cm²   b 2 cm × 8 cm = 16 cm²
10 a Triangle should have two equal sides and two equal angles
   b Triangle should have no equal sides or angles

20 Number sequences pp44–45
1 a 7, 3, −1, −5 The numbers decrease 4 each time
  b 100, 109, 118, 127 The numbers increase 9 each time
  c 136, 151, 166, 181 The numbers increase 15 each time
  d 114, 107, 100, 93 The numbers decrease 7 each time
  e 44, 52, 60, 68 The numbers increase 8 each time

2 a | −7 | −1 | 5 | **11** | 17 | **23** | 29 | **35** | **41** | 47 | 53 |

b | 303 | **293** | 283 | **273** | 263 | **253** | 243 | 233 | **223** | **213** | 203 |

c | 57 | **66** | 75 | **84** | 93 | **102** | 111 | **120** | 129 | **138** | 147 |

3 Red numbers: 7, 14, 21, 28, 35, 42, 49, 56, 63, 70, 77
  All numbers part of the 7 times table, multiples of 7, note pattern made.
  No, 100 would not be in the sequence.

Challenge yourself

a	4	8	12	16	20	24	28
b	8	16	24	32	40	48	56
c	12	24	36	48	60	72	84

8s are double 4s and 12s are 8s + 4s.

21 Multiplication and division 2 pp46–47
1 a
$$\begin{array}{r} 28 \\ \times\ 13 \\ \hline 260\ (20\times13) \\ 104\ (8\times13) \\ \hline 364 \end{array}$$
b
$$\begin{array}{r} 36 \\ \times\ 14 \\ \hline 420\ (30\times14) \\ 84\ (6\times14) \\ \hline 504 \end{array}$$
c
$$\begin{array}{r} 61 \\ \times\ 24 \\ \hline 1440\ (60\times24) \\ 24\ (1\times24) \\ \hline 1464 \end{array}$$

d
$$\begin{array}{r} 43 \\ \times\ 17 \\ \hline 680\ (40\times17) \\ 51\ (3\times17) \\ \hline 731 \end{array}$$
e
$$\begin{array}{r} 53 \\ \times\ 25 \\ \hline 1250\ (50\times25) \\ 75\ (3\times25) \\ \hline 1325 \end{array}$$
f
$$\begin{array}{r} 96 \\ \times\ 32 \\ \hline 2880\ (90\times32) \\ 192\ (6\times32) \\ \hline 3072 \end{array}$$

g   29
   × 24
  480 (20 × 24)
  216 (9 × 24)
  696

h   52
   × 38
 1900 (50 × 38)
   76 (2 × 38)
 1976

2 a 10 r2   **b** 15 r3   **c** 39 r1   **d** 22 r2   **e** 27 r2   **f** 21 r2

Challenge yourself
a 936   **b** 16

22 9 times table pp48–49

1 9, 18, 27, 36, 45, 54, 63, 72, 81, 90

2 a

9	18	**27**	**36**	45	**54**	**63**	72

b

27	**36**	**45**	54	**63**	**72**	**81**	90

c

18	**27**	36	**45**	**54**	**63**	72	**81**

3 a 45   **b** 63   **c** 54   **d** 90   **e** 27   **f** 81
4 a 54   **b** 0   **c** 81   **d** 72   **e** 63   **f** 18   **g** 36
   h 90

Challenge yourself
a 3   **b** 4   **c** 6   **d** 9   **e** 9   **f** 1   **g** 2   **h** 7   **i** 9
j 0   **k** 5   **l** 8

23 Multiples and factors pp50–51

1 b 15, 20, 50   **c** 16, 22, 10, 6   **d** 30, 90, 80
   e 18, 36, 54, 12   **f** 49, 77, 56   **g** 16, 36, 24
   h 24, 40, 56
2 a 1, 2, 4, 8   **b** 1, 3, 9   **c** 1, 2, 5, 10   **d** 1, 2, 11, 22
   e 1, 2, 3, 4, 6, 9, 12, 18, 36

Challenge yourself

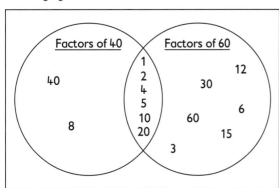

24 Square numbers pp52–53

1 b 4   **c** 5^2, 25   **d** 8^2, 64   **e** 10 × 10, 100   **f** 4 × 4, 16
2 9 16 25 36 49 64 81 100

Challenge yourself
b 1^2 **c** 5^2 **d** 4^2 **e** 10^2 **f** 9^2 **g** 6^2 **h** 8^2

25 Decimals pp54–55

1 b 12   **c** 14   **d** 18   **e** 21

2 c $19\frac{7}{10}$ **d** $36\frac{54}{100}$ **e** $67\frac{29}{100}$ **f** $59\frac{4}{10}$

3 a $2\frac{3}{4}$ **b** $4\frac{1}{2}$ **c** $6\frac{1}{4}$ **d** $3\frac{3}{4}$

Challenge yourself
2.1 $2\frac{1}{4}$ 2.3 $2\frac{1}{2}$ 2.6 2.8

26 Solving problems pp56–57

1 Yes
2 a 12   **b** 24
3 a 127   **b** 29   **c** Answers will vary

Challenge yourself
56 × 48 = 2 688 or 64 × 42

27 Capacity pp58–59

1 a 1 ml   **b** 1 litre   **c** 350 ml   **d** 3 litres   **e** 250 ml
2 Answers will vary
3 a litres   **b** ml   **c** litres   **d** litres
4 a 250 ml   **b** 450 ml   **c** 100 ml   **d** 325 ml
   e 475 ml   **f** 125 ml

Challenge yourself
a 12   **b** 20 litres

28 Line graphs pp60–61

1 a 6 am   **b** 12 noon   **c** 6°C   **d** 1°C   **e** 7°C
2

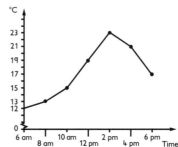

Challenge yourself
a 2 pm   **b** 11°C   **c** 19°C

How am I doing? pp62–63

1 a

28	**35**	42	**49**	**56**	63	**70**	77

b

98	**86**	74	**62**	**50**	38	**26**	14

2 a   72
   × 23
 1610 (70 × 23)
   46 (2 × 23)
 1656

b   58
   × 35
 1750 (50 × 35)
  280 (8 × 35)
 2030

3 a 17 r2   **b** 16 r1
4 a 63   **b** 36   **c** 81   **d** 27
   e 54   **f** 18
5 a 15, 50, 35   **b** 22, 18, 4   **c** 40, 90, 50   **d** 1, 2, 5, 10
   e 1, 2, 4, 8
6 a 4   **b** 16   **c** 25   **d** 100
   e 49   **f** 9
7 a $15\frac{6}{10}$ **b** $12\frac{1}{10}$ **c** $9\frac{53}{100}$ **d** $11\frac{94}{100}$
8 a ml   **b** litres   **c** ml   **d** litres

What is....

a six multiplied by eight? _____

b 3 times 8? _____

c eight eights? _____

d eight multiplied by seven? _____

e 8 multiplied by 0? _____

f ten times eight? _____

Answer these as quickly as possible.

a $4 \times 8 =$ _____   **b** $8 \times 9 =$ _____

c $8 \times 7 =$ _____   **d** $8 \times 8 =$ _____

e $8 \times 6 =$ _____   **f** $6 \times 8 =$ _____

g $0 \times 8 =$ _____   **h** $8 \times 5 =$ _____

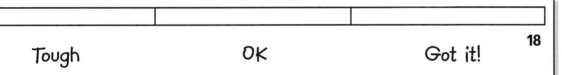

Tough	OK	Got it!

18

Total

18

More practice? Go to www

Challenge yourself

Fill in the gaps.

a _____ $\times 8 = 80$ **b** $8 \times$ _____ $= 64$ **c** _____ $\times 8 = 16$

d _____ $\times 8 = 0$ **e** $7 \times$ _____ $= 56$ **f** _____ $\times 8 = 32$

g $5 \times$ _____ $= 40$ **h** $2 \times$ _____ $= 16$ **i** _____ $\times 8 = 8$

j _____ $\times 8 = 48$ **k** _____ $\times 8 = 24$ **l** _____ $\times 8 = 72$

33

Fractions

To find $\frac{1}{2}$ of a number, divide it by **2**.

  $\frac{1}{2}$ of 6 = 3

To find $\frac{1}{5}$ of a number, divide it by **5**.

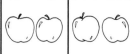  $\frac{1}{5}$ of 10 = 2

---

1. **a** To find $\frac{1}{3}$ of a number, divide it by ___3___ .

    b To find $\frac{1}{10}$ of a number, divide it by _____ .

    c To find $\frac{1}{6}$ of a number, divide it by _____ .

2. **What is ...**

    a $\frac{1}{2}$ of 10? _____   **b** $\frac{1}{4}$ of 8? _____

    c $\frac{1}{3}$ of 24? _____   **d** $\frac{1}{6}$ of 36? _____

    e $\frac{1}{4}$ of 20? _____   **f** $\frac{1}{5}$ of 35? _____

    g $\frac{1}{2}$ of 42? _____   **h** $\frac{1}{6}$ of 54? _____

    i $\frac{1}{5}$ of 25? _____   **j** $\frac{1}{3}$ of 27? _____

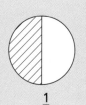 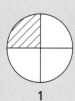

$\frac{1}{2}$ $\frac{1}{3}$ $\frac{1}{4}$ $\frac{1}{5}$ $\frac{1}{6}$ $\frac{1}{9}$ $\frac{1}{10}$

Look at the illustrated fractions on the previous page.

Now place these fractions in order of size, smallest first.

a $\frac{1}{3}$ $\frac{1}{10}$ $\frac{1}{2}$ $\underline{\frac{1}{10}}$ $\underline{\frac{1}{3}}$ $\underline{\frac{1}{2}}$

b $\frac{1}{5}$ $\frac{1}{3}$ $\frac{1}{10}$ ___ ___ ___

c $\frac{1}{6}$ $\frac{1}{3}$ $\frac{1}{4}$ ___ ___ ___

d $\frac{1}{2}$ $\frac{2}{9}$ $\frac{3}{4}$ ___ ___ ___

e $\frac{3}{10}$ $\frac{2}{3}$ $\frac{1}{5}$ ___ ___ ___

f $\frac{1}{6}$ $\frac{2}{4}$ $\frac{1}{3}$ ___ ___ ___

g $\frac{1}{6}$ $\frac{2}{10}$ $\frac{5}{9}$ ___ ___ ___

h $\frac{1}{5}$ $\frac{3}{10}$ $\frac{1}{4}$ ___ ___ ___

What fraction of the larger shape is the smaller shape?

a = $\underline{\frac{3}{5}}$

b = ___

c = ___ or $\underline{\frac{1}{2}}$

d = ___ or ___

e = ___ or ___

Tough	OK	Got it!	23

Total

23 / 23

More practice? Go to

Challenge yourself

Find the answers.

a Daniel drank 200 ml. What fraction of a litre did he drink? _____

b What fraction of a week is the weekend? _____

c Callie was awake for 18 hours on Tuesday.

What fraction of the day was she awake for? _____

d Tom's house is 400 m from school. He walks to and from school each day.

What fraction of a km does he walk in one day? _____

Mass

Mass = how heavy something is.

1 kilogram (kg) = 1000 grams **(g)**

grams

1. **Underline the correct mass for each sentence. Do you think ...**

   a a pet cat is approximately $\frac{1}{2}$ kg, 3 kg, 15 kg?

   b your pencil is approximately 5 g, 50 g, 500 g?

   c a sugar cube is approximately 1 g, 10 g, 100 g?

   d a bag of potatoes is approximately 3 kg, 100 kg, 300 kg?

   e a cup of flour is approximately 800 g, 80 g, 8 g?

2. **Suggest things you would measure in ...**

   a kilograms _____ _____ _____

   b grams _____ _____ _____

3. **Which unit of mass would you use to measure ...**

   a a mouse? _____   **b** a letter? _____

   c a computer? _____   **d** a CD case? _____

   e a T-shirt? _____   **f** a table? _____

Bathroom scales measure the weight of a person.

What weight do these bathroom scales show?

a 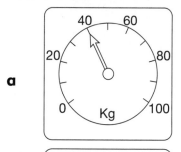 _____40_____ kg

b 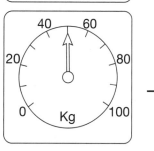 _____ kg

c  _____ kg

d  _____ kg

e 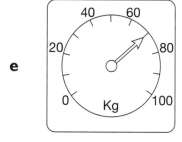 _____ kg

f _____ kg

Tough	OK	Got it!	**18**

Total

 18

More practice? Go to **www**

More practice? Go to **www**

Challenge yourself

Change this ginger-biscuit recipe for 6 people to a recipe for 12 people.

for 6 people

125 g flour
50 g   fat
75 g   sugar
2 tablespoons treacle
1 teaspoon ground ginger

for 12 people

_____ g flour
_____ g fat
_____ g sugar
_____ tablespoons treacle
_____ teaspoon ground ginger

37

Area

Area is the space **inside** a 2D shape.
To find the area of this rectangle, use square centimetres (cm^2).

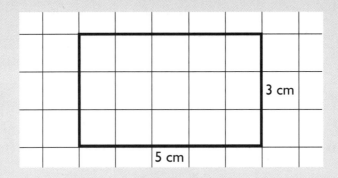

Count the number of squares inside the rectangle.
There are 15. The area is 15 cm^2.

You do not need to count the squares if you know how long the sides of the rectangle are.

Look carefully at the rectangle.
length $\times$ width $=$ area
  5 cm $\times$ 3 cm $=$ 15 cm^2
The area is 15 cm^2.

1. **Find the area of each rectangle.**

a 4 cm

5 cm

$= 5 \text{ cm} \times 4 \text{ cm} = \underline{\quad 20 \quad} cm^2$

b 2 cm

7 cm

$= 7 \text{ cm} \times 2 \text{ cm} = \underline{\qquad} cm^2$

c 4 cm

10 cm

$= 10 \text{ cm} \times 4 \text{ cm} = \underline{\qquad} cm^2$

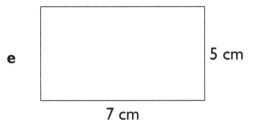

d 6 cm

3 cm

= _____ × _____ = _____ cm²

e 5 cm

7 cm

= _____ × _____ = _____ cm²

f 2 cm

10 cm

= _____ × _____ = _____ cm²

What is the area of a rectangle with...

a a length of 6 cm and width of 5 cm? _____   **b** a length of 9 cm and width of 4 cm? _____

c a length of 8 cm and width of 7 cm? _____   **d** a length of 10 cm and width of 9 cm? _____

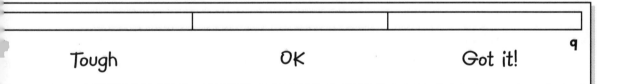

Total

Tough   OK   Got it!   9

9

More practice? Go to www

Challenge yourself

Find two more ways of halving this 6 × 6 square.

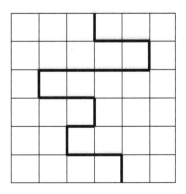
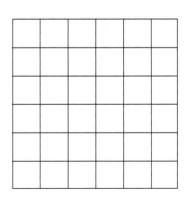
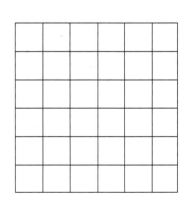

Both sides need to be equal in area.

Shape

Look carefully at these triangles.
Each triangle is slightly different.

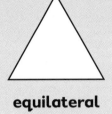

equilateral
triangle

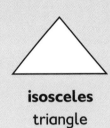

isosceles
triangle

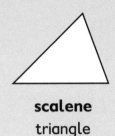

scalene
triangle

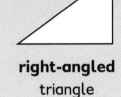

right-angled
triangle

1.   Answer these questions.

    a Which triangle has two angles equal in size? _____

    b Which triangle has no two sides equal? _____

    c Which triangle always has a 90° angle? _____

2.   Cover the triangles at the top of the page.

Now draw your own triangles.
Make each triangle slightly different to the one drawn at the top of the page. (*1 mark for eac*

equilateral triangle	isosceles triangle	scalene triangle	right-angled triangl

3.   Name this 2D shape.

The opposite sides of this shape are parallel and equal.
The diagonals bisect one another and all four angles are equal.

_____

Write an everyday object that is the same shape as these 3D shapes.

a cuboid _____

b cube _____

c cylinder _____

d sphere _____

The **net** of a 3D shape is ...
the 2D shape on paper that can be
cut out and made into the 3D shape.

Write down the 3D shapes these nets belong to.

a _____

b _____

c _____

d _____

More practice? Go to www

Challenge yourself

Draw eight nets of a cube. Each net must be different!

How am I doing?

1. **Fill in the gaps.**

   a 57 + _____ = 100

   b 28 + _____ = 100

   c _____ + 17 = 100

   d 99 + _____ = 100

2. **Fill in the gaps in the following sentences.**

   a 369 rounded to the nearest ten is _____.

   b 721 rounded to the nearest hundred is _____.

   c 3876 rounded to the nearest thousand is _____.

3. **Complete these multiplications.**

   a   23
         $\times$ 4
         _____
              (20×4)
              (3×4)
         _____
              (23×4)
         _____

   b   56
         $\times$ 5
         _____

         _____

         _____

   c   72
         $\times$ 6
         _____

         _____

         _____

4. **Divide the following.**

   a $4 \overline{)52}$

   b $6 \overline{)96}$

   c $2 \overline{)48}$

   d $5 \overline{)76}$

   e $7 \overline{)90}$

   f $3 \overline{)77}$

5. **Fill in the missing numbers.**

   a 117 − 34 = 83   83 + 34 = _____

   b 27 x 8 = 216   216 ÷ 8 = _____

   c 365 + 456 = 821   821 − 365 = _____

   d 1064 ÷ 56 = 19   56 x 19 = _____

6. **a** 3 $\times$ 8 = _____

   b 9 $\times$ 8 = _____

   c 7 $\times$ 8 = _____

   d 4 $\times$ 8 = _____

   e 5 $\times$ 8 = _____

   f 10 $\times$ 8 = _____

What is ...

a $\frac{1}{3}$ of 9? _____

b $\frac{1}{5}$ of 25? _____

c $\frac{1}{2}$ of 24? _____

d $\frac{1}{10}$ of 60? _____

e $\frac{1}{4}$ of 16? _____

f $\frac{1}{6}$ of 12? _____

What weight do these bathroom scales show?

a _____ kg

b _____ kg

c _____ kg

Find the area of each rectangle.

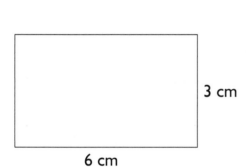

3 cm

6 cm

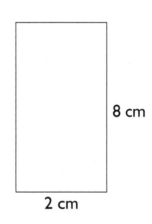

8 cm

2 cm

a _____ × _____ = _____ cm²

b _____ × _____ = _____ cm²

Draw these triangles.

a

isosceles triangle

b

scalene triangle

Total

39

More practice? Go to

Number sequences

Look at these number lines.

Rule: **the numbers decrease 6 at a time.**

67	61	55	49	43	37	31	25	19	13	7

Rule: **the numbers increase 11 at a time.**

26	37	48	59	70	81	92	103	114	125	136

1. **Finish the number sequence and write the rule.**

a

35	31	27	23	19	15	11				

Rule: _____

b

37	46	55	64	73	82	91				

Rule: _____

c

31	46	61	76	91	106	121				

Rule: _____

d

163	156	149	142	135	128	121				

Rule: _____

e

−12	−4	4	12	20	28	36				

Rule: _____

Fill in the gaps in these number lines.

a

−7	−1	5		17		29			47	53

b

303		283		263			233			203

c

57		75		93		111		129		147

Count on in 7s from 0. Colour the numbers red.

What do you notice?

_____

_____

If you went on, would 100 be in your sequence?

_____

0	1	2	3	4	5	6	7	8
9	10	11	12	13	14	15	16	17
18	19	20	21	22	23	24	25	26
27	28	29	30	31	32	33	34	35
36	37	38	39	40	41	42	43	44
45	46	47	48	49	50	51	52	53
54	55	56	57	58	59	60	61	62
63	64	65	66	67	68	69	70	71
72	73	74	75	76	77	78	79	80

Tough	OK	Got it!

9

Total

9

More practice? Go to

Challenge yourself

Complete the table below by increasing the numbers in each row...

a in 4s   b in 8s   c in 12s

a	4					
b	8					
c	12					

What do you notice?

_____

Multiplication and division

Do you remember?

$$\begin{array}{r} 36 \\ \times\ 7 \\ \hline 210 \\ 42 \\ \hline 252 \\ \hline \end{array}$$

$210 \quad (30 \times 7)$
$42 \quad (6 \times 7)$
$252 \quad (36 \times 7)$

Look carefully at how we multiply even bigger numbers.

$$\begin{array}{r} 36 \\ \times\ 17 \\ \hline 510 \\ 102 \\ \hline 612 \\ \hline \end{array}$$

$510 \quad (30 \times 17)$
$102 \quad (6 \times 17)$
$612 \quad (36 \times 17)$

1. Find the answers.

Use the space provided to work out your answers.

a
$$\begin{array}{r} 28 \\ \times\ 13 \\ \hline \\ \hline \\ \hline \end{array}$$

b
$$\begin{array}{r} 36 \\ \times\ 14 \\ \hline \\ \hline \\ \hline \end{array}$$

c
$$\begin{array}{r} 61 \\ \times\ 24 \\ \hline \\ \hline \\ \hline \end{array}$$

d
$$\begin{array}{r} 43 \\ \times\ 17 \\ \hline \\ \hline \\ \hline \end{array}$$

e
$$\begin{array}{r} 53 \\ \times\ 25 \\ \hline \\ \hline \\ \hline \end{array}$$

f
$$\begin{array}{r} 96 \\ \times\ 32 \\ \hline \\ \hline \\ \hline \end{array}$$

g
$$\begin{array}{r} 29 \\ \times\ 24 \\ \hline \\ \hline \\ \hline \end{array}$$

h
$$\begin{array}{r} 52 \\ \times\ 38 \\ \hline \\ \hline \\ \hline \end{array}$$

Watch out! When you divide some numbers there will be remainders. **67 ÷ 4 = ?**

$$\begin{array}{r} 1\ 6\ \ \text{r}3 \\ 4\overline{)6\,{}^27} \end{array}$$

67 ÷ 4 = 16 r3

Find the answers (including remainders!).
Use the space provided to work out your answers.

a 62 ÷ 6 = _____

b 78 ÷ 5 = _____

c 79 ÷ 2 = _____

d 68 ÷ 3 = _____

e 83 ÷ 3 = _____

f 86 ÷ 4 = _____

			Total
Tough	OK	Got it!	

14

14 / 14

More practice? Go to www

Challenge yourself

Solve these problems.

a Harry is helping pick apples from an apple orchard.
He picks 24 apples from each tree.
There are 39 apple trees. How many apples does he pick? _____

b Nina is helping pick the plums. She has picked 112 plums from 7 trees. If each tree
gave the same number of plums, how many plums did each tree provide? _____

9 times table

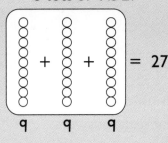

3 lots of 9 is 27

= 27

9   9   9

3   ×   9   =   27

1. $1 \times 9 =$ _____ $6 \times 9 =$ _____

$2 \times 9 =$ _____ $7 \times 9 =$ _____

$3 \times 9 =$ _____ $8 \times 9 =$ _____

$4 \times 9 =$ _____ $9 \times 9 =$ _____

$5 \times 9 =$ _____ $10 \times 9 =$ _____

2. **Finish the 9 times table number sequences.**

a

9	18			45			72

b

27			54				90

c

			45			72	

What is...

a 9 times 5? _____

b nine sevens? _____

c nine multiplied by six? _____

d nine times ten? _____

e 9 multiplied by 3? _____

f nine nines? _____

Answer these as quickly as possible.

a $6 \times 9 =$ _____

b $9 \times 0 =$ _____

c $9 \times 9 =$ _____

d $8 \times 9 =$ _____

e $9 \times 7 =$ _____

f $9 \times 2 =$ _____

g $4 \times 9 =$ _____

h $9 \times 10 =$ _____

Tough	OK	Got it!

18

Total

18

More practice? Go to

Challenge yourself

Fill in the gaps.

a _____ $\times 9 = 27$

b _____ $\times 9 = 36$

c _____ $\times 9 = 54$

d $9 \times$ _____ $= 81$

e $10 \times$ _____ $= 90$

f _____ $\times 9 = 9$

g _____ $\times 9 = 18$

h _____ $\times 9 = 63$

i $3 \times$ _____ $= 27$

j $9 \times$ _____ $= 0$

k _____ $\times 9 = 45$

l _____ $\times 9 = 72$

Multiples and factors

A **multiple** is a number that can be divided **exactly** by a smaller number.

30, 15, 10, 25, 45 are all multiples of **5**.

All these numbers divide exactly by 5.

1. **Ring the numbers in the box that are multiples of**

a 3

| 8 | (18) | 25 | (30) | (24) | 5 | (21) |

b 5

| 15 | 18 | 32 | 20 | 43 | 7 | 50 |

c 2

| 27 | 16 | 33 | 22 | 19 | 10 | 6 |

d 10

| 69 | 30 | 45 | 90 | 38 | 80 | 21 |

e 6

| 59 | 18 | 61 | 36 | 21 | 54 | 12 |

f 7

| 38 | 49 | 77 | 9 | 22 | 39 | 56 |

g 4

| 9 | 55 | 37 | 29 | 16 | 36 | 24 |

h 8

| 67 | 24 | 40 | 19 | 56 | 79 | 25 |

A **factor** is a number that can be divided **exactly** into a bigger number.

15 has 4 numbers that divide equally into it.

1, **3**, **5** and **15** are factors of **15**.

15 has 4 factors.

List the factors for these numbers.

a 8   _____ _____ _____ _____

b 9   _____ _____ _____

c 10   _____ _____ _____ _____

d 22   _____ _____ _____ _____

e 36   _____ _____ _____ _____ _____ _____ _____ _____ _____

Tough	OK	Got it!	**12**

Total

	12

More practice? Go to www

Challenge yourself

Complete this Venn diagram to find the factors common to both 40 and 60.

Factors of 40   Factors of 60

51

Square numbers

The square of a number is the number multiplied by itself.

Write the calculation like this ... $3^2 = 9$

$$3 \times 3 = 9$$

$$3 \quad 3 \quad 3 = 9$$

Look!

When the answer is drawn it looks like a square.

---

1. **Fill in the gaps.**

a $6 \times 6 = 6^2 =$ $= \underline{36}$

b $2 \times 2 = 2^2 =$ $= \underline{\hspace{2cm}}$

c $5 \times 5 = \underline{\hspace{2cm}} =$ $= \underline{\hspace{2cm}}$

d $8 \times 8 = \underline{\hspace{2cm}} =$ $= \underline{\hspace{2cm}}$

e $\underline{\hspace{2cm}} \times \underline{\hspace{2cm}} = 10^2 =$ $= \underline{\hspace{2cm}}$

f $\underline{\hspace{2cm}} \times \underline{\hspace{2cm}} = 4^2 =$ $= \underline{\hspace{2cm}}$

Answer the following.

1^2 = _1_

2^2 = _4_

3^2 = _____

4^2 = _____

5^2 = _____

6^2 = _____

7^2 = _____

8^2 = _____

9^2 = _____

10^2 = _____

Use this space to continue drawing the squares in order.
Draw a square around the shape.

Tough	OK	Got it!

6

Total

 6

More practice? Go to

More practice? Go to www

Challenge yourself

Which number squared gives the following answers?

a 49 _7^2_

b 1 _____

c 25 _____

d 16 _____

e 100 _____

f 81 _____

g 36 _____

h 64 _____

Decimals

In decimals, the **decimal point** (·) separates the whole numbers from the numbers that are less than 1. Everything before the decimal point is a whole number. Everything after it is a fraction.

| 10 | 11 | 12 |

10·2   10·89   11·5   11·91

Look at the arrows and decimals written below the number line.

10·2 is equivalent to 10 whole numbers and **2 tenths**.
11·91 is equivalent to 11 whole numbers and **91 hundredths**.

1. **Round to the nearest whole number.**

   a   10·15 rounded to the nearest whole number is ___10___.

   b   12·32 rounded to the nearest whole number is _____.

   c   13·9 rounded to the nearest whole number is _____.

   d   17·6 rounded to the nearest whole number is _____.

   e   21·23 rounded to the nearest whole number is _____.

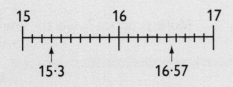

15   16   17

15·3   16·57

15 whole numbers and 3 tenths
15·3 can also be written as a **mixed number** $15\frac{3}{10}$

16 whole numbers and 57 hundredths
16·57 can also be written as a mixed number $16\frac{57}{100}$

2. **Write each of these decimal numbers as a mixed number.**

   a   16·81 = ___$16\frac{81}{100}$___   b   21·36 = ___$21\frac{36}{100}$___

   c   19·7 = _____   d   36·54 = _____

   e   67·29 = _____   f   59·4 = _____

Do you remember?

$\frac{5}{10}$ is the same as $\frac{1}{2}$ $\frac{5}{10} = \frac{1}{2}$

So **2.5 = $2\frac{1}{2}$**

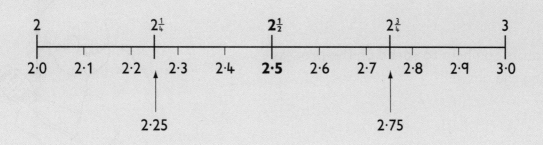

Match the equivalent numbers with a line.

a 2.75 ●

b 4.5 ●

c 6.25 ●

d 3.75 ●

● $6\frac{1}{4}$

● $2\frac{3}{4}$

● $3\frac{3}{4}$

● $4\frac{1}{2}$

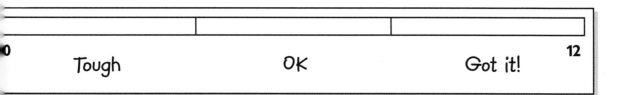

Tough   OK   Got it!   **12**

Total

More practice? Go to www

Challenge yourself

Write these numbers in order, smallest first.

| **2·1** | **2·3** | **2$\frac{1}{2}$** | **2·8** | **2$\frac{1}{4}$** | **2·6** |

2·1

___   ___   ___   ___   ___   ___

Solving problems

Solving problems in maths is a way of playing with numbers. Approach each problem as a challenge!

Calculators can help to speed up the process of finding the answer.

1. Is it true that the product of any two consecutive numbers is even? _____

2. 2 squares can make 1 rectangle,

   and 4 squares can make 2 different rectangles.

   a How many squares are needed to make three different rectangles? _____

   b How many squares are needed to make four different rectangles? _____

a Ben thinks of a number.
He adds 23 and divides it by 5.
The answer is 30.

What is the number Ben first thought of? _____

b Ashley thinks of a number.
She subtracts 21 and multiplies it by 9.
The answer is 72.

What is the number Ashley first thought of? _____

c Now write your own problem.
Complete the gaps below and then try it out on someone!

I think of a number.

I _____ and _____.

The answer is _____.

What is the number I first thought of? _____

| Tough | OK | Got it! | **6** |

Total

6

More practice? Go to www

Challenge yourself

Each △ represents a missing digit. They can be different numbers.

Use a calculator to help you complete the number sentence.

$$\triangle\triangle \times \triangle 4 \triangle = 2\,688$$

Capacity

Capacity = the amount of space inside something

1 Litre

1 litre **(l)** = 1000 millilitres **(ml)**

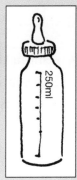

250ml

1. **Underline the correct capacity for each sentence. Do you think ...**

   a a raindrop is approximately   1 ml,   100 ml,   500 ml?

   b a carton of milk is approximately   1 l,   10 l,   100 l?

   c a mug is approximately   35 ml,   350 ml,   3 500 ml?

   d a family-sized ice-cream tub is approximately   0.3 l,   3 l,   30 l?

   e a jam jar is approximately   2 ml,   25 ml,   250 ml?

2. **Suggest things you would measure in ...**

   a litres    _____ _____ _____

   b millilitres _____ _____ _____

3. **Which unit would you use to measure ...**

   a the capacity of a bath?   _____

   b the capacity of an egg cup? _____

   c a bottle of lemonade?   _____

   d the capacity of a fish tank? _____

Cylinders with millilitres marked on the side can be used to measure capacity. Read the capacities below.

a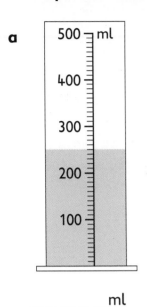

_____ ml

b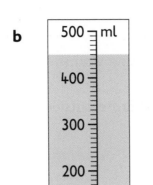

_____ ml

c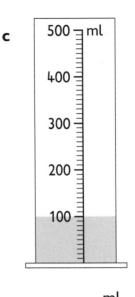

_____ ml

d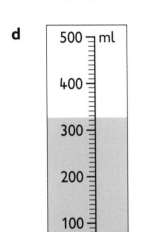

_____ ml

e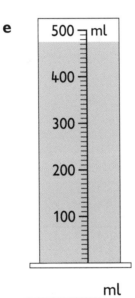

_____ ml

f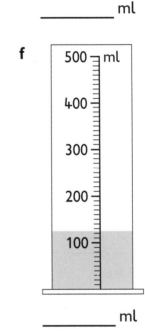

_____ ml

Tough	OK	Got it! **17**

Total

17

More practice? Go to www

Challenge yourself

Solve these problems.

a   Dad makes 3 litres of soup on Bonfire night. One cup of soup holds 250 ml.
    How many people can have a cup of soup? _____

b   A car is filled with 20 000 millilitres of petrol. How many litres is this? _____

Line graphs

A **line graph** shows information in a simple way.

The line graph below shows the temperature outside on a day in January.

QUICK TIP!
The dots on a line graph are joined to **clearly** show the changes made over time.

Temperature on 24th January

°C
12 –
11 –
10 –
9 –
8 –
7 –
6 –
5 –
4 –
3 –
2 –
1 –

6 am   8 am   10 am   12 pm   2 pm   4 pm   6 pm   Time

1. **Look at the line graph and answer the following questions.**

    a At what time was the temperature 1°C? _____

    b At what time was the temperature at its highest point? _____

    c What is the temperature at 4 pm? _____

    d How much did the temperature drop between 12 noon and 2 pm? _____

    e How many degrees did the temperature rise from 6 am to 12 noon? _____

Draw a line graph showing the following information.

Remember to join the dots.

(8 marks: 1 per dot, 1 for line)

The temperature on 31st July							
Time	6 am	8 am	10 am	12 noon	2 pm	4 pm	6 pm
°C	12	13	15	19	23	21	17

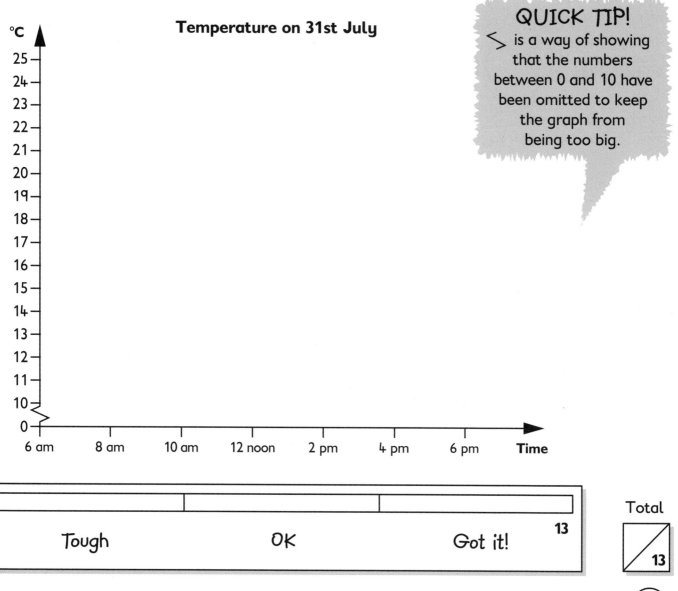

Temperature on 31st July

QUICK TIP!

⟨ is a way of showing that the numbers between 0 and 10 have been omitted to keep the graph from being too big.

Tough   OK   Got it!   **13**

Total

13

More practice? Go to

Challenge yourself

Use the graph you have drawn to answer the following questions.

a What was the hottest time of the day? _____

b How many degrees did the temperature rise between 6 am and 2 pm? _____

c What was the temperature at 12 noon? _____

1. **Fill in the gaps in the number lines.**

a

28		42			63		77

b

98		74			38		14

2. **a**   7 2
          ×   2 3
          ───────

          ───────
          ───────

b   5 8
          ×   3 5
          ───────

          ───────
          ───────

3. **a** 70 ÷ 4 = _____   **b** 97 ÷ 6 = _____

4. **a** $7 \times 9 =$ _____   **b** $4 \times 9 =$ _____

 c $9 \times 9 =$ _____   **d** $9 \times 3 =$ _____

 e $9 \times 6 =$ _____   **f** $2 \times 9 =$ _____

Ring the numbers in the box that are multiples of ...

a 5

| 21 | 36 | 15 | 46 | 50 | 35 | 6 |

b 2

| 13 | 22 | 37 | 18 | 7 | 4 | 9 |

c 10

| 18 | 40 | 31 | 90 | 28 | 64 | 50 |

List the factors for these numbers.

d 10

_____ _____ _____ _____

e 8

_____ _____ _____ _____

Work out the following square numbers.

a $2^2 =$ _____

b $4^2 =$ _____

c $5^2 =$ _____

d $10^2 =$ _____

e $7^2 =$ _____

f $3^2 =$ _____

Write these numbers as fractions.

a $15.6 = 15 \frac{}{10}$

b $12.1 =$ _____

c $9.53 =$ _____

d $11.94 =$ _____

Which unit, litres or millilitres, would you use to measure the capacity of a ...

a mug? _____

b bucket? _____

c baby bottle? _____

d paddling pool? _____

Total

31

More practice? Go to

Try the 10–11 years book

Lesson 1

Calculations

Do you remember which are odd and which are even numbers?

2 4 6 8 10 = **even numbers**
1 3 5 7   9 = **odd numbers**

Here are some quick, simple rules that will help you check the possibility of your answers being right.

- **The sum of two even numbers is even:**
  3612 + 5876 = answer will be an even number

- **The sum of two odd numbers is even:**
  6577 + 2183 = answer will be an even number

- **The sum of one odd and one even number is odd:**
  3657 + 2186 = answer will be an odd number

> **QUICK TIP!**
> Knowing these rules helps you check whether an answer is reasonable or not!

1. **Write whether these answers will be odd or even.**

   a 218 + 567 = _odd_

   b 369 + 217 = _____

   c 1856 + 3962 = _____

   d 3691 + 1285 = _____

   e 9999 + 111 = _____

   f 317 + 5896 = _____

   g 7963 + 7962 = _____

> **QUICK TIP!**
> Again, knowing this can help you check whether an answer is reasonable.

Remember ... there are ways of checking addition, subtraction, multiplication and division number sentences by changing them round.

Look at these.
587 + 623 = 1210   1210 − 623 = 587
381 × 19 = 7239   7239 ÷ 381 = 19